The Ants' Party

Original story by Nick Beare
and Jeanette Greenwell

Illustrated by Matt

Andy Ant is in his house.
His house is in the garden.
It's under a tree.

Andy's very happy.
There's a party today in the garden.

There's a hat competition.
There are prizes.

What's the matter, Andy?

I haven't got a hat.

Andy Ant is in the kitchen.
He's sad.

Here's a hat, Andy!

Oh, but it's very old, Dad. I don't like it.

Don't worry!
I've got an idea!

Now Andy has got a new hat!
It's got stars, moons and shapes.
It's yellow, purple, green, red and blue.

Do you like your hat now, Andy?

Yes! My hat is fantastic!

Andy is ready for the party.

Goodbye, Andy! Have a lovely time!

This hat is very, very big!

Betty is wearing a small, blue hat. It's got yellow flowers.

Hello, Betty! I like your hat.

Thanks, Andy!

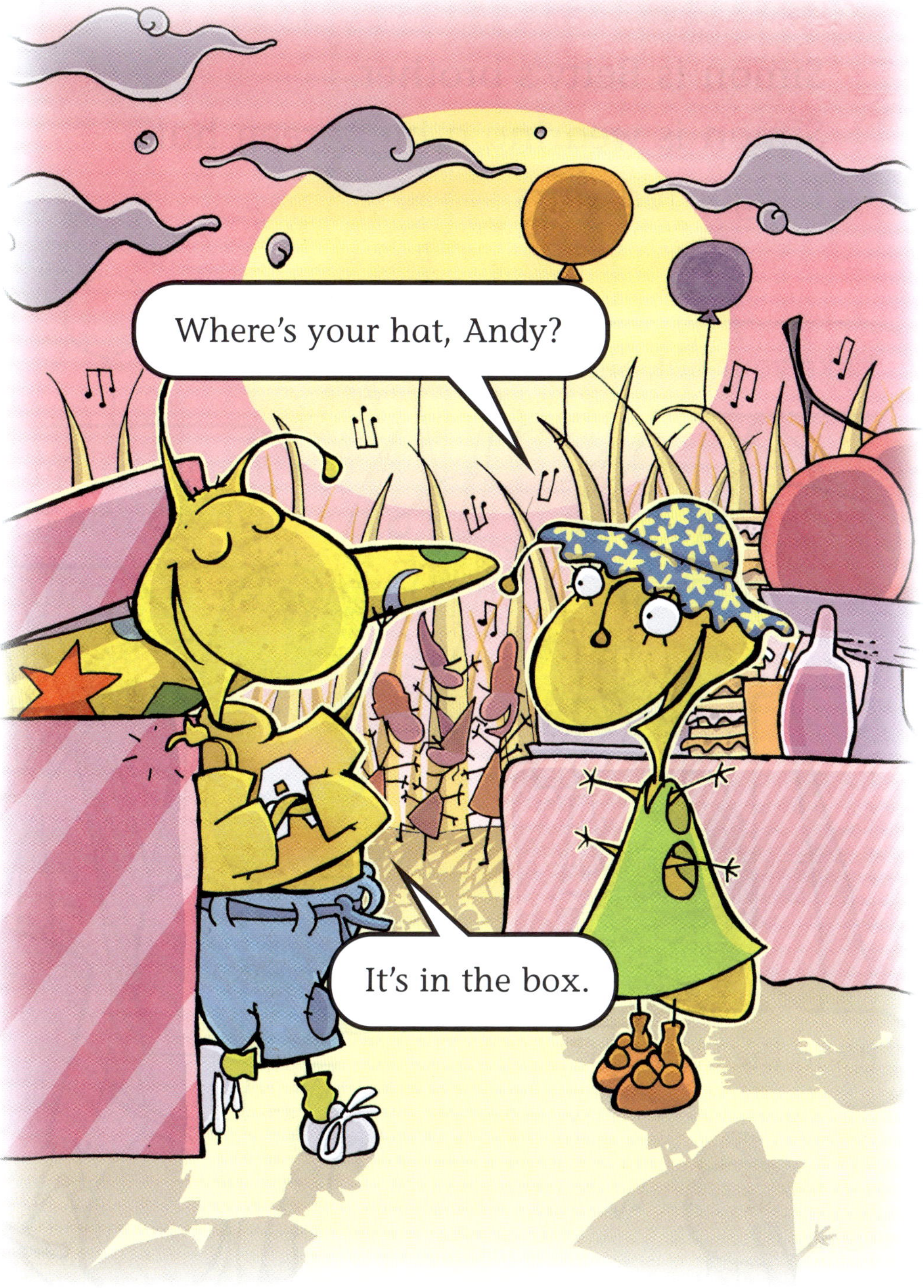
Where's your hat, Andy?
It's in the box.

Simon is Betty's brother.
Simon is wearing a big, green hat.
It's got red stars.

I like your hat, Simon.

Thank you, Andy. Where's your hat?

It's in the box.

Look at all the ants! Look at all the hats!
Can you see …
> A green hat?
> A blue hat?
> A yellow hat?
> A red hat?
> A purple hat?

The party is fantastic!
Look at all the food on the table!
Ice cream, popcorn, sandwiches
and hot dogs!

Mmmm! I'm hungry.

So am I!

Listen! It's the King Ant.
It's time for the hat competition.

And now the winner of the competition is ...

It's raining.
The ants are very sad.

Andy has got an idea!
His very big hat is in the box.

Now all the ants are under Andy's hat.
Everybody's very happy.
It's a great party!

Andy is the winner of the hat competition.

Hurray for Andy!

Activities

1 Read and circle the correct hat.

It's a red hat with blue flowers, yellow shapes and green stars.

2 Read and colour the hats.

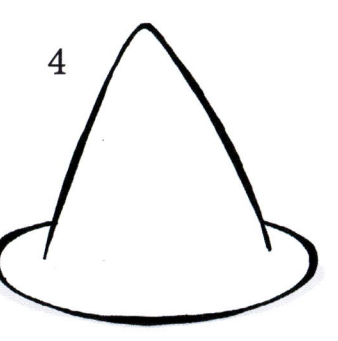

1 A blue hat with yellow stars.
2 A yellow hat with purple shapes.
3 A red hat with green flowers.
4 A green hat with purple stars.

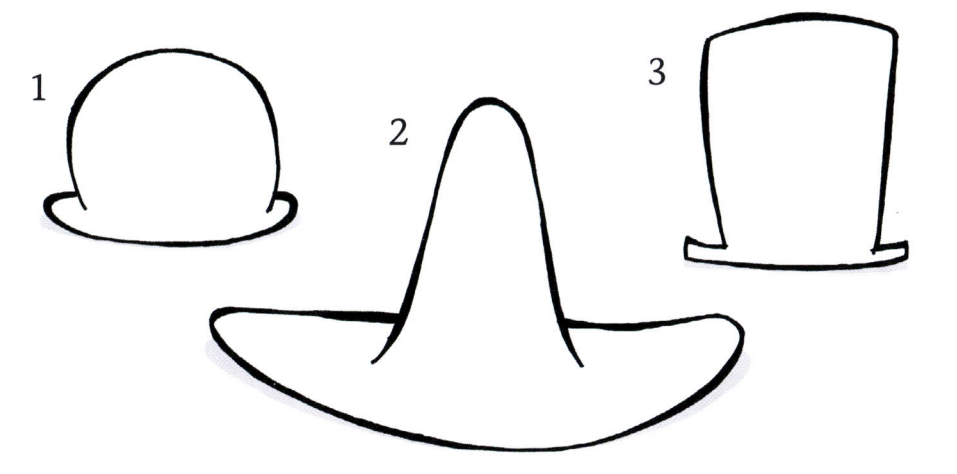

3 Circle the correct word.

1 He's big/small.

2 He's happy/sad.

3 She's happy/sad.

4 It's small/big.

5 It's old/new.

6 It's new/old.

4 Write about the hats.

I'm wearing a <u>small</u>, _____ hat.
It's got <u>yellow</u> _____.

I'm wearing a _____, _____ hat.
It's got _____ _____.

5 Where's Andy? Match.

He's under the tree.

He's in the box.

He's on the table.

6 Write *in*, *on* or *under*.

1 The cat is _____ the tree.

2 The cat is _____ the box.

3 The cat is _____ the hat.

4 The cat is _____ the table.

5 The cat is _____ the table.

6 The cat is _____ the hat.

7 Choose and write five sentences about house A and five sentences about house B.

1 _____

2 _____

3 _____

4 _____

5 _____

1 _____

2 _____

3 _____

4 _____

5 _____

There are two flowers.
The house is small.
There's a box on the table.
The house is big.
There are eight flowers.

There's a hat in the box.
There's a cat in the box
There's a box under the tree
The house is blue.
The house is red.

8 Write.

ice cream
popcorn
sandwiches
hot dogs

9 Complete.

Mmmm! I'm hungry. I like _____ and _____.

So am I! I like _____ and _____.

Picture Dictionary

house	garden	tree	hat
competition	prize	winner	party
happy	sad	flowers	box
table	big	small	rain

shapes	stars	moon	new
old	under	in	on
popcorn	sandwich	hot dog	ice cream
blue	red	green	purple	yellow

Macmillan Education
4 Crinan Street
London N1 9XW
A division of Springer Nature Limited
Companies and representatives throughout the world

ISBN 978-1-4050-2504-1
ISBN 978-1-4050-5729-5 (International Edition)

First published 1998 Springer Nature Limited
This edition © Springer Nature Limited 2004

All rights reserved; no part of this publication may be reproduced, stored in a retrieval system, transmitted in any form, or by any means, electronic, mechanical, photocopying, recording, or otherwise, without the prior written permission of the publishers.

Illustrated by Carlos Matera

Printed and bound by Ashford Colour Press Ltd.

2020 2019
25 24